Chai
MY JEWISH LIFE JOURNAL

Student Book

Curriculum Core for Grade 2

Torah, Avodah, G'milut Chasadim

Name:_____

Printed on acid-free paper
Copyright © 2002 by UAHC Press
Manufactured in the United States of America
10 9 8 7 6 5 4 3 2

TORAH JOURNAL

Introduction To Torah

In our lesson devoted to the genesis of the world (which means God's creation of the world), we talked about the fact that we are partners with God in maintaining all that has been created.

Discuss with your parent(s) how we are responsible for helping to keep God's creations safe.

What is it that you do to help keep God's creations safe?_____

_____

When we study Torah, we are able to learn about our relationship to God, our relationship with other people and our relationship with the world.

What do you and your parents hope to learn by studying Torah?_____

_____

My Creation

Student's Name _____

Date _____

1. The name of my creation is _____

2. My creation lives in _____

3. I need to give my creation the following things for it
   to live well:_____

Date_____

Dear Parents:

Each week your children will receive an assignment to be completed in their TORAH JOURNAL. It is our belief that by studying Torah, we can learn how to better live and conduct our lives as Jews and as B'nai Adam (human beings). We suggest you take the time each week to sit down with your child and let him or her tell you what has been done and learned in school about Torah. This way your child will turn from student into teacher, and together your family will have the opportunity to share new learning. Some of the home assignments will also require your help and participation: these are all contained in the TORAH JOURNAL, where there are also Torah texts and readings included for you to get a better grasp of what we have done in class. As time goes on, you will find that the TORAH JOURNAL is a wonderful working and teaching tool to use with your child in examining, understanding, and cherishing the world around us.

Thank you for your important involvement in your child's study.

Sincerely,

_____

Introduction to the Book of *Sh'mot*

Discuss with your parent(s) the following questions, and write down your responses in the space provided:

1. What is the best part of being a member of a group?_____

   _____

   _____

2. What is the hardest part of being a member of a group?_____

   _____

   _____

Finding God in Small Places

Moses was able to see God in a little thorn bush and, because he stopped and noticed God in the bush, God was able to ask him to free the Israelites from Egypt. If Moses hadn't stopped long enough to really look at the bush and to finally notice that it wasn't burning up, he would have not heard God and freed the Israelites and we, the Jews, would not be here today as a free people.

1. During the course of the week, it's your turn to be like Moses and notice God in all kinds of unusual places. Bring your blessing sheet with you wherever you go and try to notice one thing every day over which you can say a blessing. In particular try to notice something special about what you do every day. You might want to take the sheet with you when you go shopping with a parent or on a walk together and see if you notice something that you want to say a blessing over. Remember, it doesn't have to be especially beautiful or big. It should be something you notice that you don't usually notice.

2. Write down here what you blessed and which blessing you used for it. Give a short description of what you saw that was godly and special, and what the "uniqueness" or "magic" of this object was.

This week I said a *b'rachah* when I...

_____

_____

_____

_____

Here's what was special or godly about
what I saw or did...

_____

_____

_____

_____

When I said the blessing it made me feel...

_____

_____

_____

_____

Blessings for Daily Life

Upon Seeing Lightning

Blessed are You, *Adonai*, our God, Ruler of the universe, Who makes the work of creation.

בָּרוּךְ אַתָּה יְיָ אֱלֹהֵינוּ מֶלֶךְ הָעוֹלָם, עֹשֶׂה מַעֲשֵׂה בְרֵאשִׁית.

Upon Hearing Thunder

Blessed are You, *Adonai*, our God, Ruler of the universe, Whose strength and power fill the universe.

בָּרוּךְ אַתָּה יְיָ אֱלֹהֵינוּ מֶלֶךְ הָעוֹלָם, שֶׁכֹּחוֹ וּגְבוּרָתוֹ מָלֵא עוֹלָם.

Upon Seeing A Rainbow

Blessed are You, *Adonai*, our God, Ruler of the universe, for You remember the covenant, You are faithful to Your covenant and You fulfill Your word.

בָּרוּךְ אַתָּה יְיָ אֱלֹהֵינוּ מֶלֶךְ הָעוֹלָם, זוֹכֵר הַבְּרִית וְנֶאֱמָן בִּבְרִיתוֹ וְקַיָּם בְּמַאֲמָרוֹ.

Upon Admiring Natural Beauty
(of things, wildlife, or people)

Blessed are You, *Adonai*, our God, Ruler of the universe, Whose world is filled with such beauty.

בָּרוּךְ אַתָּה יְיָ אֱלֹהֵינוּ מֶלֶךְ הָעוֹלָם, שֶׁכָּכָה לּוֹ בְּעוֹלָמוֹ.

Upon Seeing Unusual People or Animals

Blessed are You, *Adonai*, our God, Ruler of the universe, Who makes creatures different.

בָּרוּךְ אַתָּה יְיָ אֱלֹהֵינוּ מֶלֶךְ הָעוֹלָם, מְשַׁנֶּה הַבְּרִיּוֹת.

Upon Seeing the First Seasonal Blossom of the Trees

Blessed are You, *Adonai*, our God, Ruler of the universe, for You have made in Your universe good creatures and good trees in which to please humankind.

בָּרוּךְ אַתָּה יְיָ אֱלֹהֵינוּ מֶלֶךְ הָעוֹלָם, אֲשֶׁר בָּרָא בְּעוֹלָמוֹ בְּרִיּוֹת טוֹבוֹת וְאִלָנוֹת טוֹבִים, לְהָנוֹת בָּהֶם בְּנֵי אָדָם.

Parashat Bo: Marking Our Freedom
Session א (*Alef*)

At Home

Many Jews place a mezuzah on the front door of the house and on the doorway to every room in their home, except for the bathrooms. When walking into each room, the mezuzah is a reminder that God is in that room (in every room) and that the room is special, just as the blood on the door of Israelite homes in Egypt indicated that the Israelites were about to go free and reminded God not to harm the people in the marked homes.

With a parent, discuss the following questions and write down your answers:

1. On the door of which room in my house would I like to place a mezuzah?

_____

_____

_____

2. What is special about the room that I would like to remember each time I enter it?

_____

_____

_____

3. What other special things would I like to be reminded of as I walk into that room?

_____

_____

_____

NOTE TO THE PARENT: Your child will be asked to use the answers to these questions in the creation of their own mezuzah for the room she or he has chosen.

Parashat Bo: Marking Our Freedom
Session ב (*Bet*)

Affix the mezuzah by a room of your choice. Do the following exercise:

- During the week, as you enter this room, try to notice the mezuzah and think about what it reminds you of.
- Pass by and pay attention to your mezuzah for a few days before answering the following questions:

1. When I notice my mezuzah, I think about_____
_____

2. What do I feel when I think about the special things my mezuzah reminds me of?_____
_____

3. What other Jewish ways do I have to remind myself of special things every day?_____
_____

Parashat B'shalach:
Nachshon Comes to Visit

In Class

Using your own story, write or draw your "miracle."

[If you have difficulties representing your miracle story, ask your teacher for help, or Nachshon himself!]

At Home

Show your work to your parent(s), explain what we have talked about in class and then together with them complete the following statement:

This story of miracles made me think of...

_____

_____

_____

_____

_____

_____

Parashat Yitro: Helping Hands

In Class

1. Make your own list of "Characteristics of a Good Helper," helping yourself with the list from the Torah text and the list you made in class.

2. Answer the following: "What characteristics will help me be a good partner to people who need help?"

At Home

"I was like Moses because I needed help. Here's what I needed help with..."

a. Think about a time you needed help in your life and didn't ask for it. You can sit down with your parent(s) and have them help you remember a situation in which you could have really used some help. Write down what happened, why, and how you needed help.

b. Using the list of characteristics you prepared, write how someone might have been able to help you; what kind of person this ideal helper should have been (his or her characteristics).

I was like Moses because I needed help. Here's what I needed help with_____

_____

_____

_____

_____

_____

Parashat Ki Tisa:
Hold On To Your Hat, God!

In Class or At Home

Write one or two pieces of advice you could use the next time you have to deal with someone who is angry (with you, or with someone else):

1._____

_____

_____

_____

2._____

_____

_____

_____

Parashat Mishpatim:
Reaching Out To Strangers

Together with your parent(s), look back at the pages you filled out during this Torah course in your **TORAH JOURNAL** and answer the following two questions:

What was your favorite *parashah* (Torah portion)? Why?

_____

_____

_____

Of all the things you learned in and from the Torah, what do you think is the most important for your life? Why?

_____

_____

_____

חֲזַק חֲזַק וְנִתְחַזֵּק

CHAZAK, CHAZAK V'NITCHAZEK!

BE STRONG, BE STRONG
AND MAY YOU BE STRENGTHENED!

Parashat Mishpatim

You shall not wrong a stranger or oppress him, for you were strangers in the land of Egypt.

Exodus 22:20

You shall not oppress a stranger, for you know the feelings of the stranger, having yourselves been strangers in the land of Egypt.

Exodus 23:9

SEFER AVODAH
MY JEWISH
WORKBOOK

Why Can't I See God?

Think back to all the things we discussed in class about "seeing" God in the world around us, and complete the following sentence:

I see God's imprint in the world ...... (where? when?)

_____

_____

_____

_____

_____

_____

Shabbat Blessings

Celebrating Shabbat at Home

a) Assignment with a camera:

This week it is your turn to celebrate Shabbat with your family and show the class what it was like, this special, "extraordinary" day in your home. Take two or three pictures yourself (or ask a parent to help you) of those moments that best represent the way you and your family have celebrated Shabbat together this week.

Ask your parent(s) to help you complete the Shabbat Celebration Journal on the next page, which will be shared with your classmates during our next lesson.

b) Assignment without a camera:

Ask your parent(s) to help you complete the Shabbat Celebration Journal on the next page, which will be shared with your classmates during our next lesson. You may choose to answer the questions in writing or draw pictures.

Family Shabbat Celebration Journal

Our Names _____ _____

_____ _____

_____ _____

_____ _____

Date_____

This week we celebrated Shabbat by...

We did these special activities_____

_____

We ate these special foods_____

_____

The day felt special because_____

_____

We felt close to God when/because_____

_____

Parent Resources for Shabbat Celebration

1. Perelson, Ruth. *Invitation to Shabbat*.
    New York: UAHC Press, 1997.
    Everything you ever wanted to know about Shabbat in an accessible volume that assumes no prior knowledge.

2. Rauchwerger, Lisa. *Chocolate Chip Challah and Other Twists on the Jewish Holiday Table*.
    New York: UAHC Press, 1999.
    This interactive cookbook for families is filled with a variety of delicious holiday treats, as well as information about the various holidays. It is designed for parents and children to use together.

3. Shapiro, Mark Dov. *Gates of Shabbat*.
    New York: CCAR Press, 1990.
    This book is a how-to, with answers to any questions you might have about the whys and hows of Jewish ritual and practice. Information on Friday night blessings can be found on pp. 14–32, 15, 20, 23-24, 27. (Teachers may choose to include these pages in the packet sent home.)

4. Olitzky, Kerry M. and Ronald H. Isaacs. *The How-to Handbook for Jewish Living*.
    Hoboken, N.J.: KTAV Publishing House, 1993.
    A step-by-step guide with text references and additional recommended resources.

5. *Do It Yourself Shabbat*.
    Prepared by the Family Education Committee of the UAHC-CCAR Commission on Jewish Education.
    This is a handy, fold-out, washable card written with both traditional and single-parent households in mind. http://uahc.org/educate/

6. Zwerin, Raymond A. and Marcus Audrey Friedman. *Shabbat Can Be*.
    New York: UAHC Press, 1979.
    A wonderful, warm story about exactly what this lessons hopes families will do!

Internet resources:

http://www.jewish.com/holidays/shabbat.shtml—Basic holiday information.

http://judaism.about.com/culture/religion/jud—Basic holiday information.

http://uahc.org/clickonj/pages/shabbat02.htm—An article on just where to start when introducing Shabbat celebration in your home.

http://uahc.org/shabbat/index.shtml—"Shabbat Family Table Talk." Family discussion suggestions for the weekly Torah portion.

Shabbat Blessings

For the candles

בָּרוּךְ אַתָּה יְיָ אֱלֹהֵינוּ מֶלֶךְ הָעוֹלָם, אֲשֶׁר
קִדְּשָׁנוּ בְּמִצְוֹתָיו, וְצִוָּנוּ לְהַדְלִיק נֵר שֶׁל שַׁבָּת.

*Baruch atah Adonai, Eloheinu Melech haolam, asher kid'shanu
b'mitzvotav v'tzivanu l'hadlik ner shel Shabbat.*

Blessed are You, *Adonai* our God, Ruler of the Universe, who sanctifies
us by Your commandments and commands us
to kindle the lights of Shabbat.

For the wine

בָּרוּךְ אַתָּה יְיָ אֱלֹהֵינוּ מֶלֶךְ הָעוֹלָם, בּוֹרֵא פְּרִי הַגָּפֶן.

Baruch atah Adonai, Eloheinu Melech haolam, borei p'ri hagafen.

Blessed are You, *Adonai* our God, Ruler of the Universe,
who creates the fruit of the vine.

For the challah

בָּרוּךְ אַתָּה יְיָ אֱלֹהֵינוּ מֶלֶךְ
הָעוֹלָם, הַמּוֹצִיא לֶחֶם מִן הָאָרֶץ.

Baruch atah Adonai, Eloheinu Melech haolam,
hamotzi lechem min ha-aretz.

Blessed are You, *Adonai* our God, Ruler of the Universe,
who brings forth bread from the earth.

MOTZI: WE THANK GOD FOR THE GIFT OF BREAD

Date_____

Dear Parents:

Our last lesson was centered on Shabbat. We explored how celebrating Shabbat by doing something really special, that we don't have time to do during the week, is a way of making Shabbat truly holy and it is part of Avodah—the work of the heart to find sacred connections to God, community, and self. We would appreciate it if your family could take a moment to sit down together and complete the Shabbat Celebration Journal over the next few weeks.

In class we discussed the teaching of the prophet Isaiah, who said that celebrating Shabbat means to take time out from the ordinary. So, next Shabbat, we invite you to do something different that you don't do every day—whether it's lighting candles at the dinner table on Friday night, saying blessings together, attending synagogue, or cooking a special dish that you all particularly enjoy. Students came up with several different suggestions for what they think could make their Shabbat "special": don't forget to ask your child(ren) to share with you the list of ideas generated in class. In addition, students learned the Motzi blessing for Erev Shabbat (Friday night).

We are including several resources that might help you with your home Shabbat celebrations: blessings in Hebrew, English and transliteration, and a resource sheet which lists websites and books for you and your child(ren). We hope that you will find celebrating Shabbat an enjoyable family activity, and we look forward to hearing about and learning from your experience.

Sincerely,

_____

Morning Blessings

At Home

Think about what you have learned in class today: the importance of connecting to God at the very start of each day, when we wake up in the morning. According to Judaism, thanking God for the new day we are given is part of *avodah*, the work of the heart we do to find sacred connections to God. Thinking about the things you can be happy about and thankful for when you wake up in the morning, complete the following open sentence:

On this new day I am thankful to God because...

_____

_____

_____

Repeat this exercise at least three times before our next class.

Date_____

Dear Parents:

As part of our ongoing learning about avodah, the "work" we do to find sacred connections to God, community, and self, today we have studied in class the blessing Modeh Ani. These two Hebrew words (that literally mean "I give thanks") open the traditional morning prayer we recite to thank God for the new day of life we are given to experience. It is the Jewish way of taking the time to stop and connect to God just before the busy routine of our daily lives sets in and grabs all our attention and strength. Students have written and decorated beautiful poems about expressing gratefulness to God that will help them remember to thank God each morning.

Over the next week, we hope that you will try to say this blessing with your child(ren). Students have also been assigned the homework of completing the sentence "On this new day I am thankful to God because..." at least three times during the coming week. Remind your child(ren) to do the assignment and bring it to the next class. You may want to add your own thoughts to this journal (SEFER AVODAH) as well. We would love to hear them. It would probably help if your child kept his or her SEFER AVODAH by the bed, so that completing the sentence and thinking of God at the start of every new day will become a ritual.

Thank you for your participation.

_____

Sh'ma

Complete the following open sentence:

When I listen to God, I hear...

_____

_____

_____

Share this sheet with your parents and tell them what we learned about the *Sh'ma*, our most important Jewish prayer. Put this sheet by your bed during the week and try to recite the prayer at least once before you go to bed. Think about how saying this prayer makes you feel at night. Write down your thoughts to bring with you next week and share with the class if you want.

שְׁמַע יִשְׂרָאֵל יְיָ אֱלֹהֵינוּ יְיָ אֶחָד:

Sh'ma Yisrael Adonai Eloheinu Adonai Echad

Hear, Israel, *Adonai* is our God, *Adonai* is One.

בָּרוּךְ שֵׁם כְּבוֹד מַלְכוּתוֹ לְעוֹלָם וָעֶד.

Baruch Shem k'vod malchuto l'olam va-ed

Blessed is God's glorious kingdom for ever and ever.

Thoughts for Next Class:

When I said the *Sh'ma* at night I felt ...

_____

_____

_____

When I listened for God, I could hear ...

_____

_____

_____

Evening Blessings

Fill out the two parts of the following sentence:

Saying the *Sh'ma* at night will make me feel...because...

Saying the *Sh'ma* at night will make me feel_____

_____

_____

_____

_____

because_____

_____

_____

_____

_____

Date_____

Dear Parents:

During our previous lesson, we studied the words to the most important prayer of the Jewish people, the Sh'ma. Students had been asked to share with you some of the things learned in class about the Sh'ma: our uniqueness as a people, and our ability to feel close to God when we recite this prayer and pay attention to its words. We hope that you saw the homework and that your child shared some of these ideas with you last week.

Today your child(ren) brought home a Sh'ma pillow cover. We have worked on this special project for two weeks. It would be ideal if students could attach this cover to a special pillowcase, or even wrap it around a special stuffed animal, so that they can keep it close each night as they sleep.

We spent the last two lessons talking about the Sh'ma and its centrality in our belief. We learned how to say this prayer with deep concentration in order to be able to hear God— each of us in his or her own special way. We spent a great deal of time on this art project, trying to think of pictures and colors that would make each student feel warm and safe at night. Jews everywhere recite the Sh'ma at night to remind themselves of the connection to the One God. By turning our thoughts toward God and repeating ancient words of our tradition, we transform ordinary bedtime into special Jewish time, thus helping children understand that being Jewish is a way of life, something we do inside and outside the synagogue and especially within the walls of our homes. We hope that this art project will inspire you and your children to say this prayer each night before you go to bed.

Thank you for your interest and participation in your child(ren)'s Jewish learning.

Sincerely,

_____

How do I talk to God?

Blessing: WHAT ARE YOU THANKFUL FOR?

- In class you thought of some things you are thankful to God for. How can you say, "Thank You, God," for those good things in your life?

- Remember how the boy in the story we read in class used his skills to say thanks to God. Take time to think of your own way to best thank God. You can put it in writing, or create an artwork or drawing that represents your thankfulness. *Don't forget the six Hebrew words you learned in class—they might come handy now if you choose to write your personal "Thank You" note to God for the good things in your life.

I Thank God

בָּרוּךְ אַתָּה יְיָ אֱלֹהֵינוּ מֶלֶךְ הָעוֹלָם

Baruch atah Adonai, *Eloheinu Melech haolam*

Blessed are you, Adonai *our God,*
Ruler of the Universe

Thank You God

Why Does God Want Me to Grow?

Now that you are growing up, you should pay special attention to all the things you can do to help other people—things you weren't capable of doing when you were just a baby. Every time you help someone else or do something kind for others (it could be at school, at home, or anywhere else you are), we will write this on our class bulletin board GROWING UP—DOING MY PART.

Complete the following open sentences:

I can help others by...

_____

_____

_____

When I help others I feel like God's partner, because...

_____

_____

_____

Date _____

Dear Parents:

This week in class, we learned about how to "hear" God and how to talk to God through prayer and action. Next week we will be talking about how God helps us grow and how, as we grow up, we are better able to take care of ourselves and even help others.

Part of our exploration will focus on how each student is now different from when he or she was a baby. To help facilitate this discussion, please send in a picture of your child as a baby. Make sure that it is a reprint, a spare copy, or an original you don't mind becoming part of an art project that will remain in our school. Together the class will be creating a bulletin board titled "GROWING UP-DOING MY PART." We invite you to come see it and also to take part in it. Return the bottom of this letter with your child's picture and take the time to share with your child some memories of when he or she was little.

At each class for the next several weeks, we will be adding details to this bulletin board of how the students are doing things (in school or at home) to help other people and bring wholeness to our world; this process is called tikkun olam. If your child does something special or particularly kind that you think is worth mentioning on our bulletin board, please drop me a note or stop by to share it.

Thank you for your participation. We look forward to putting together this very special project with you.

Sincerely,

_____

Please fill out and return with the baby picture:

Our child's name is _____

Our favorite thing to watch _____ do when

he/she was a baby was_____

Now that _____ is growing up,

we are proud that he/she has learned to

_____

Photo
Here

How Does God Talk to Me?

Today I felt good about myself because...

_____

_____

_____

_____

_____

When I feel good about myself, I think that God...

_____

_____

_____

_____

_____

Does God Know Me?

My Own Special Way of Connecting With God

Take time to discuss with your parents all you learned about *avodah*—our way to make sacred connections to God. Think about the many things we did in class to connect with God: we wrote blessings of thanks, we thought about what we can do to help others, we learned blessings and prayers, celebrated Shabbat, heard stories, and so much more!

Think about how God made you unique, about the ways in which you are a different and special individual. Share your thoughts with your parents. Which ideas and thoughts explored through the study of *avodah* would you like to remember forever? You may want to make a list with your parents, then craft the items on your list into a poem, a scrapbook-type collage, or even a blessing (using the blessing starter words we learned, "Blessed are you, *Adonai* our God, Ruler of the Universe"). No matter what form you decide to give to your collection of thoughts, memories, and ideas from the unit we shared together, this work will become your special *avodah*, your own unique way of connecting with God.

After you have written your blessing, find the proper time to recite it. Then, answer the following questions:

1. What was special about saying this blessing?
2. How did it make you feel to have your own blessing?
3. What do you suppose God thinks of your blessing?

Date_____

Dear Parents:

Today we completed our unit on Avodah-the prayer, ceremonies, and celebrations we do to find sacred connections to God, community, and self. We have tried to develop an understanding of what it means to communicate with the Divine: through formal prayer, through actions that help others, and through better understanding ourselves. As a culminating activity for the unit, each student was asked to craft his or her own special Avodah. This way, they will create a "tool" to connect with God by remembering all they have learned from this unit and modeling it into a special page of memories, whether in the form of an art project, poem, prayer, or scrapbook-type collage. We have sent home a worksheet to guide them, but we hope that you will work with them as well.

Some wonderful parent resources for talking about God with children are:
· Harold Kushner. When Children Ask about God. New York: Random House, 1995.
· David J. Wolpe. Teaching Your Children About God. New York: HarperCollins, 1995.

We suggest that you have your children explain what they have learned from this study. Your guiding questions may include:

1. The concept of b'tzelem Elohim, being created in God's image (from Genesis 1:27). Ask them to share the worksheet they completed in class today!
2. Why we can't see God, and how we can feel God's help and know God talks to us. (Students learned that God helps us by making us grow, and that God talks to us by helping us feel good about what we can do for others.)
3. Thankfulness. Ask them what they are thankful for, why, and how they express this thankfulness.
4. Ask them what they did during the week that helped them feel good about themselves and helped someone else.

Be sure to share with them some of your feelings and your answers to these questions. Try to complete the worksheet together and have the student return it to class next week. If you have any questions or would like some help with this assignment, please do not hesitate to call.

Looking forward to hearing your child's special blessing,

Sincerely,

_____

G'MILUT CHASADIM
DIARY

Making a difference

Take the picture drawn in class and glue it below, on this first page of your *G'MILUT CHASADIM DIARY.*

OR:

Draw a new image of yourself doing another act of *g'milut chasadim.*

Write down under your picture a short sentence describing what is you are doing and why this is an act of loving-kindness (*g'milut chasadim*).

GLUE YOUR DRAWING OR PICTURE HERE

THIS IS ME_____

THIS IS AN ACT OF *G'MILUT CHASADIM* BECAUSE_____

_____

name:_____ date:_____

The act of *g'milut chasadim* that I did:

Where I did it:_____

When I did it:_____

For whom I did it:_____

With whom I did it:_____

How it made me feel:_____

What I learned by doing it:_____

What was *kadosh* (holy) about this act of loving-kindness:_____

Draw a picture or attach a photo of yourself doing your act of *g'milut chasadim.*

Torah Teaches Us

Write what you learned about these acts of *g'milut chasadim* from the Torah stories:

נֶחָמָה

Comforting the mourner   *Nechamah*

מַלְבִּישׁ עֲרֻמִּים

Clothing the naked   *Malbish arumim*

בִּקּוּר חוֹלִים

Visiting the sick   *Bikur cholim*

מַאֲכִיל רְעֵבִים

Feeding the hungry   *Maachil r'eivim*

הַכְנָסַת אוֹרְחִים

Welcoming guests/strangers   *Hachnasat orchim*

וְאָהַבְתָּ לְרֵעֲךָ כָּמוֹךָ

Treating people with kindness   *V'ahavta l'rei-acha kamocha*

צַעַר בַּעֲלֵי חַיִּים

Being kind to animals   *Tzaar baalei chayim*

כִּבּוּד זְקֵנִים

Honoring the Elderly   *Kibud Z'keinim*

In God's Image

I am like God when I_____

_____

_____

_____

_____

_____

_____

_____

_____

Being God's Partner

What are some of the ways you can be God's partner?

_____

_____

_____

_____

_____

_____

Welcoming Guests

What are some of the things you can do to make guests feel welcome in your home?

(List as many things as possible and ask your parents to help you think of ways to do *Hachnasat Orchim.*)

_____

_____

_____

_____

_____

_____

Taking Action

"No one should let a day pass without doing a specific act of loving-kindness, whether by giving money or by a personal action."

Isaiah Horowitz

What do these words mean to you? Explain them in your own words.

_____

_____

_____

What have YOU done today that has been loving and kind to others?

_____

_____

_____

Reflections on Doing Acts
of *G'milut Chasadim*

G'milut chasadim is:

_____

_____

_____

It's important to do *g'milut chasadim* because:

_____

_____

_____

Some acts of *g'milut chasadim* that we have learned about are:

_____

_____

_____

My Reflections Worksheet

Last week my *g'milut chasadim* activity was_____
_____

• I knew I was helping when..._____
_____

• I think my act of *g'milut chasadim* made a difference in the world because..._____
_____

• I think that the people or the community that I helped felt..._____
_____

• The most important thing I remember about my *g'milut chasadim* experience is..._____
_____

G'MILUT CHASADIM DIARY

Celebrations

Make a list of some of the ways you can include *g'milut chasadim* in your birthday celebrations.

_____

_____

_____

_____

_____

_____

_____

_____

_____